MATHEMATICS 506

CONTENTS

Author: **Carol Bauler, B.A.**
Editor: Alan Christopherson, M.S.
Graphic Design: JoAnn Cumming, A.A.

Alpha Omega Publications ®

300 North McKemy Avenue, Chandler, Arizona 85226-2618

I. Part One

Objectives

To add and subtract fractions
To learn about 2-dimensional and 3-dimensional figures
To solve missing number problems

1.1 Describe each number as ...

a. proper fraction b. improper fraction c. mixed number

$\frac{9}{6}$ ________ $1\frac{3}{5}$ ________ $\frac{5}{8}$ ________ $\frac{7}{2}$ ________

$2\frac{1}{3}$ ________ $\frac{4}{7}$ ________ $\frac{12}{3}$ ________ $\frac{9}{10}$ ________

1.2 Write in words.

$\frac{3}{8}$ ____________________ $\frac{7}{9}$ ____________________

$\frac{3}{2}$ ____________________ $\frac{6}{5}$ ____________________

$5\frac{2}{5}$ ____________________ $7\frac{4}{9}$ ____________________

The factors of a number are all of the numbers that, when multiplied together, produce a given number. Factors are written in number order.

1.3 Write all of the facts that are equal to 8.

x 8 x 8 x 8 ___ x 8 ______ ______ ______

What four numbers make up the facts for 8? ______, ______, ______, ______

What are the factors of 8? ______, ______, ______, ______

Write all of the facts that are equal to 12.

___x___ 12 ___x___ 12 ___x___ 12 ___x___ 12 ___x___ 12 ___x___ 12

What six numbers make up the facts for 12? _____, _____, _____, _____, _____, _____

What are the factors of 12? _____, _____, _____, _____, _____, _____

What is the largest factor common to 8 and 12? ________

What is the largest number that will divide evenly into 8 and 12? ________

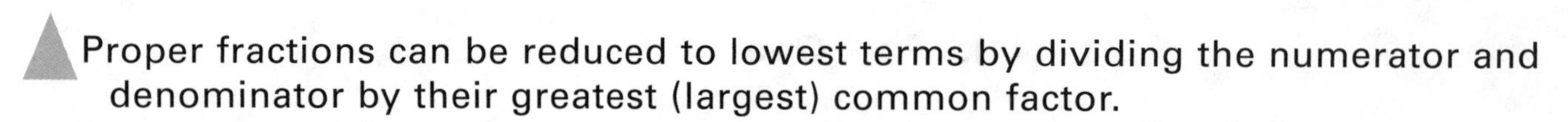
Proper fractions can be reduced to lowest terms by dividing the numerator and denominator by their greatest (largest) common factor.

1.4 Reduce proper fractions to lowest terms.

$\frac{8}{12} =$ $\qquad \frac{14}{16} =$ $\qquad \frac{12}{18} =$ $\qquad \frac{20}{25} =$ $\qquad \frac{9}{15} =$ $\qquad \frac{15}{21} =$

Improper fractions can be reduced to lowest terms by dividing the denominator into the numerator. Write the remainder as a fraction.

1.5 Reduce improper fractions to lowest terms.

$\frac{9}{8} =$ $\qquad \frac{14}{3} =$ $\qquad \frac{11}{5} =$ $\qquad \frac{21}{8} =$ $\qquad \frac{6}{3} =$ $\qquad \frac{7}{4} =$

Improper fractions may need to be further reduced.

$\frac{4}{8}$ can be reduced to $\frac{1}{2}$. $\qquad \frac{12}{8} = 1\frac{4}{8} = 1\frac{1}{2}$

1.6 Reduce improper fractions to lowest terms.

$\frac{14}{4} = \quad =$ $\qquad \frac{26}{6} = \quad =$ $\qquad \frac{22}{8} = \quad =$

1.7 Follow the steps to add or subtract fractions and mixed numbers.
Add or subtract fractions. Reduce fractions to lowest terms.
Add or subtract whole numbers.

a. $\frac{3}{8} + \frac{1}{8}$ $\qquad \frac{5}{9} + \frac{7}{9}$ $\qquad \frac{3}{7} + \frac{4}{7}$ $\qquad \frac{11}{12} - \frac{5}{12}$

b. $\frac{5}{6} - \frac{1}{6}$ $\qquad \frac{3}{4} - \frac{1}{4}$ $\qquad 5\frac{1}{4} + 2\frac{1}{4}$ $\qquad 4\frac{2}{3} + 5\frac{1}{3}$

c. $6\frac{2}{9} + 8\frac{4}{9}$ $\qquad 8\frac{1}{2} - 3\frac{1}{2}$ $\qquad 7\frac{5}{8} - 6\frac{3}{8}$ $\qquad 4\frac{9}{10} - 2\frac{4}{10}$

Multiples of numbers are the products of the number.

1.8 Write five multiples for 6 and 8.

$1 \times 6 =$ ______ $2 \times 6 =$ ______ $3 \times 6 =$ ______ $4 \times 6 =$ ______ $5 \times 6 =$ ______

$1 \times 8 =$ ______ $2 \times 8 =$ ______ $3 \times 8 =$ ______ $4 \times 8 =$ ______ $5 \times 8 =$ ______

Write multiples in number order for ...

6: ______, ______, ______, ______ 8: ______, ______, ______, ______

Write the smallest common multiple for 6 and 8. ________

Fractions *must* have the same denominator to be added or subtracted.
Find a common denominator by finding the smallest common multiple.

The common denominator of $\frac{5}{6}$ and $\frac{3}{8}$ is 24.
Change $\frac{5}{6}$ and $\frac{3}{8}$ to equivalent fractions.
Divide the denominators and multiply the numerators.

$\frac{5}{6} = \frac{20}{24}$ $24 \div 6 = 4$ $4 \times 5 = 20$

$\frac{3}{8} = \frac{9}{24}$ $24 \div 8 = 3$ $3 \times 3 = 9$

1.9 Name the common denominator. Write the new fraction (s).

$\frac{3}{4}, \frac{7}{8}$ ________ ____ = ____ $\frac{5}{8}, \frac{3}{10}$ ________ ____ = ____ ____ = ____

1.10 Follow the steps to add or subtract fractions and mixed numbers.
Write equivalent fractions. Add or subtract.
Reduce answers to lowest terms. Add or subtract whole numbers.

a. $\frac{3}{4} + \frac{2}{8}$ $\frac{5}{6} + \frac{2}{3}$ $\frac{3}{10} + \frac{1}{5}$ $\frac{3}{4} - \frac{1}{3}$ $\frac{11}{12} - \frac{1}{4}$

b. $2\frac{4}{5} + 4\frac{2}{3}$ $7\frac{2}{4} + 3\frac{2}{5}$ $6\frac{7}{9} - 4\frac{2}{6}$ $8\frac{5}{8} - 5\frac{1}{4}$

Rectangles lie flat on a surface.
They have length and width.
They are two-dimensional figures.
(L) 5 inches (W) 3 inches

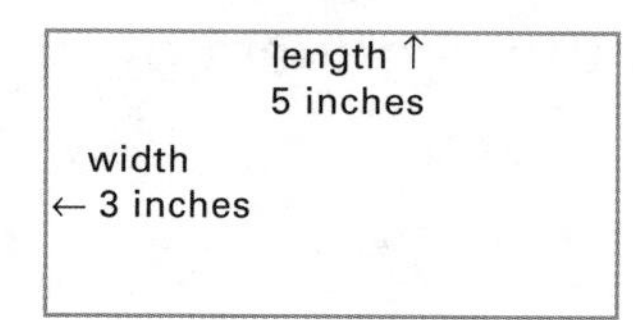

Rectangular solids take up space.
They have length, width, and height.
They are three-dimensional figures.
(L) 5 inches (W) 3 inches (H) 4 inches

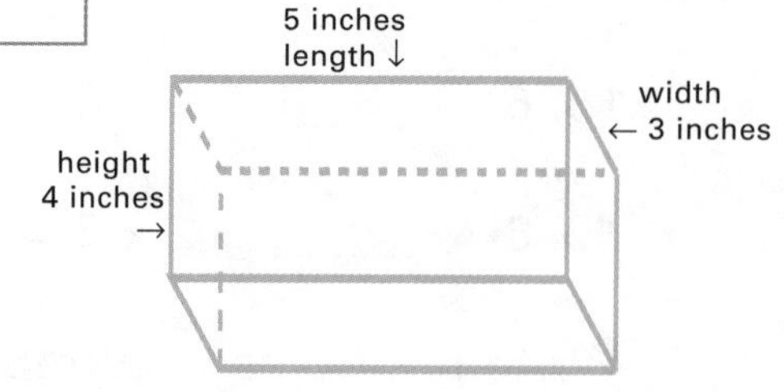

Rectangles are measured by finding the perimeter or area.
Perimeter is measured in *linear* inches, area in *square* inches.

1.11 Find the perimeter and area measurement for the rectangle in the illustration. *Label answers correctly.*

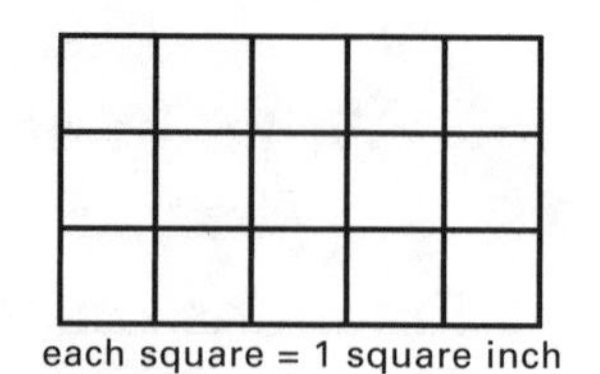

P = (2 x L) + (2 x W) A = L x W

P = ______________________ A = ______________________

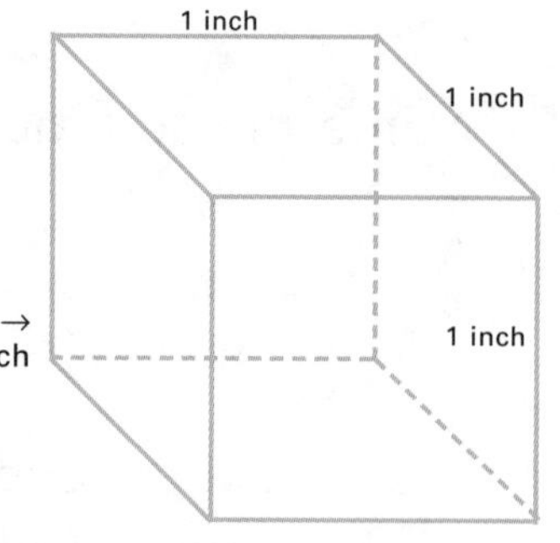

Rectangular solids are measured by finding the **volume**.
Volume is measured in cubic inches.
A cubic inch looks like a block.

1.12 Imagine that you could cover the bottom of the rectangular solid shown at the top of the page with a layer of cubic inches.
How many cubic inches would you need? __________

How many layers would it take to fill the solid? __________

How many cubic inches to fill the whole solid? __________

The formula for volume is length times width times height.

1.13 Use the formula to find the volume for the rectangular solid at the top of the page. V = L x W x H

Is the answer the same as the answer to ex. 1.12? __________ V = ______________________

Number sentences show a relationship between values.

Peter is 65 in. tall. Melinda is 62 in. tall.

The number sentence reads ... $65 \text{ in.} > 62 \text{ in.}$ *or* $65 \text{ in.} \neq 62 \text{ in.}$

1.14 Write each of the following sentences in two number sentences.

a. The band class lasted 49 minutes on Tuesday and 53 minutes on Thursday.

____________________ ____________________

b. Patricia earned $9.75 babysitting and $5.50 doing errands.
Jennifer earned $16.45 at a bake sale.

____________________ ____________________

An equation is a number sentence that contains an equal sign.

John and Rita bought four boxes of popsicles that cost $2.73 each.
Altogether, John and Rita spent $10.92.

The equation reads ... 4 x $2.73 = $10.92

1.15 Write each of the following sentences as an equation.

a. Mr. Jones drove his car for 5 hours at a rate of 63 miles per hour. He drove 315 miles. ____________________

b. The room has a length of 9 feet and width of 5 feet. The perimeter is 28 linear feet. ____________________

An equation may have a missing number (N).

Jason did 28 pushups each day for 7 days.
How many pushups did he do altogether?

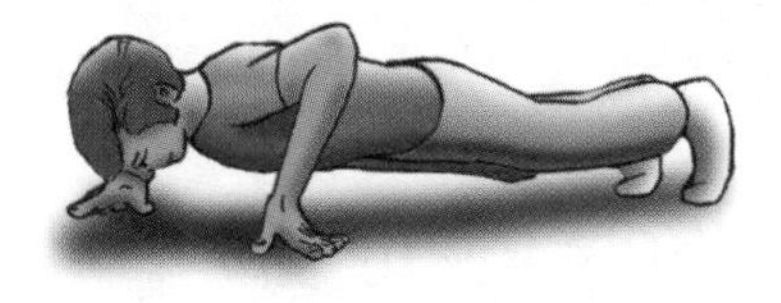

The equation reads $7 \times 28 = N$ $196 = N$

1.16 Write the number sentences as equations with a missing number.
Write the value of the missing number.

a. Colleen answered 67 questions out of 75 correctly on her test. How many questions did she have marked wrong? ____________________

____

b. Kevin spent $15.60 of the $25 that he had saved for a new watch. How much money did Kevin have after paying for the new watch? ____________________

____

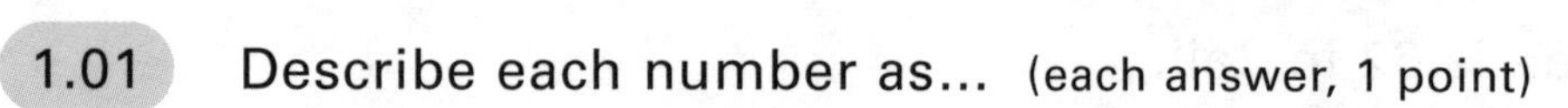

Self Test 1

1.01 Describe each number as... (each answer, 1 point)

a. proper fraction b. improper fraction c. mixed number

$2\frac{1}{8}$ ________ $\frac{3}{2}$ ________ $\frac{6}{7}$ ________

1.02 Write in words. (each answer, 1 point)

$\frac{7}{8}$ ______________________ $6\frac{4}{5}$ ______________________

1.03 What are the factors of 9? ____, ____, ____ (1 point)

What are the factors of 12? ____, ____, ____, ____, ____, ____ (1 point)

What is the largest factor common to 9 and 12? ______ (1 point)

1.04 Reduce or simplify fractions to lowest terms. (each answer, 1 point)

$\frac{5}{3} =$ $\frac{12}{8} =$ $\frac{3}{18} =$

1.05 Follow the steps to add or subtract fractions and mixed numbers. Reduce fractions to lowest terms. (each answer, 1 point)

$\frac{4}{9} + \frac{6}{9}$ $\frac{3}{8} + \frac{1}{8}$ $\frac{11}{12} - \frac{5}{12}$ $3\frac{1}{2} + 4\frac{1}{2}$ $7\frac{5}{8} - 2\frac{3}{8}$ $9\frac{5}{6} - 2\frac{1}{6}$

1.06 Write the first four multiples for ... (3 points)

4: ____, ____, ____, ____ 6: ____, ____, ____, ____

Write the smallest multiple that 4 and 6 have in common. ____

1.07 Follow the steps to add or subtract fractions and mixed numbers. Write equivalent fractions. Reduce answers to lowest terms. (each answer, 1 point)

$\frac{7}{8} + \frac{3}{4}$ $\frac{3}{5} - \frac{4}{15}$ $6\frac{7}{16} - 3\frac{3}{8}$ $8\frac{2}{3} - 4\frac{1}{2}$

1.08 Write the formula for perimeter and area. (4 points)
Find the perimeter and area measurement for the rectangle in the illustration. *Label answers correctly.*

7 feet
3 feet

P = A =

P = ______________ A = ______________

1.09 Write the formula for volume. (2 points)
Find the volume for the rectangular solid in the illustration.

2 feet
5 feet
3 feet

V =

V = ______________

1.010 Write the following sentence in two number sentences. (each answer, 1 point)

Becky and Ashlee were both saving money from baby-sitting jobs.
Becky had 8 dollars, 6 quarters, and 2 nickels.
Ashlee had 9 dollars, 1 quarter, and 5 dimes.

______________ ______________

1.011 Write the number sentence as an equation with a missing number.
Write the value of the missing number. (2 points)

Joseph's father drives 18 miles to work each day.
How many miles does he drive in 5 days?

____

______________ = N

27/34

My Score ______________

Teacher Check ______________

II. Part Two

Objectives
To multiply fractions To show data on a picture graph To borrow in subtraction of fractions

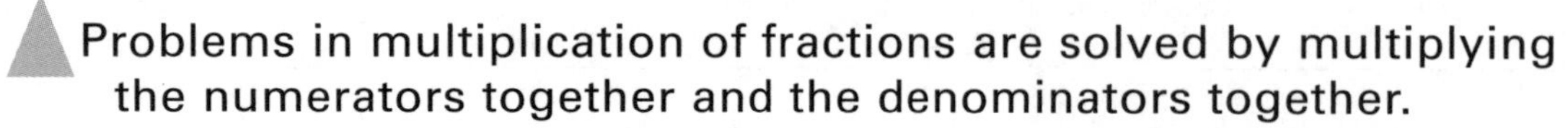

Problems in multiplication of fractions are solved by multiplying the numerators together and the denominators together.

If possible, answers should be simplified or reduced to lowest terms.

$\frac{1}{4} \times \frac{1}{2} = \frac{1}{8}$ $\qquad$ $\frac{2}{5} \times \frac{5}{6} = \frac{10}{30} = \frac{1}{3}$

2.1 Multiply.

a. $\frac{1}{2} \times \frac{5}{7} =$ $\qquad$ $\frac{3}{5} \times \frac{2}{6} =$ $\qquad$ $\frac{1}{4} \times \frac{2}{3} =$ $\qquad$ $\frac{3}{7} \times \frac{1}{2} =$

b. $\frac{3}{8} \times \frac{1}{3} =$ $\qquad$ $\frac{2}{5} \times \frac{1}{10} =$ $\qquad$ $\frac{2}{7} \times \frac{2}{3} =$ $\qquad$ $\frac{1}{6} \times \frac{3}{5} =$

Multiplication of fractions can be understood by substituting the word "of" for the multiplication sign. Study the illustration.

$\frac{1}{3} \times \frac{1}{4} = \frac{1}{12}$ $\qquad$ *or* $\qquad$ $\frac{1}{3}$ of $\frac{1}{4} = \frac{1}{12}$

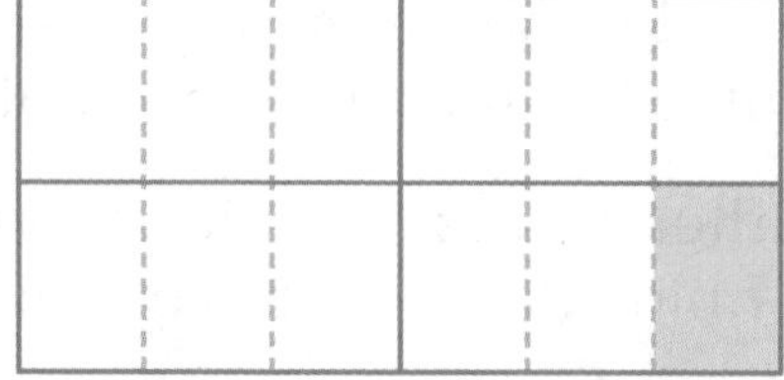

← $\frac{1}{3}$ of $\frac{1}{4} = \frac{1}{12}$

2.2 Solve the problems in multiplication of fractions. (Do not simplify answers.) Color the part of the drawing that illustrates your answer.

a.

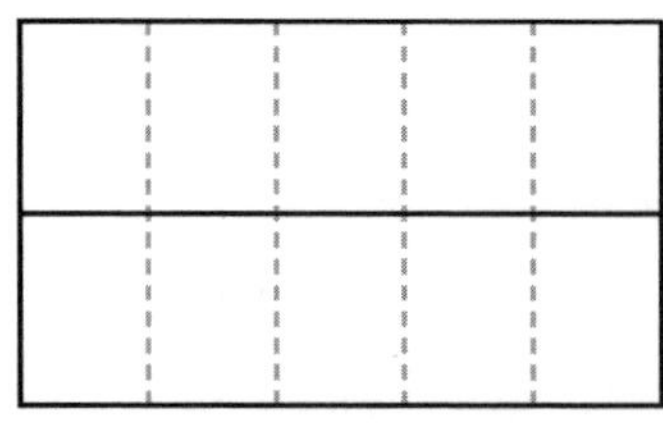

$\frac{2}{5}$ of $\frac{1}{2} =$

b.

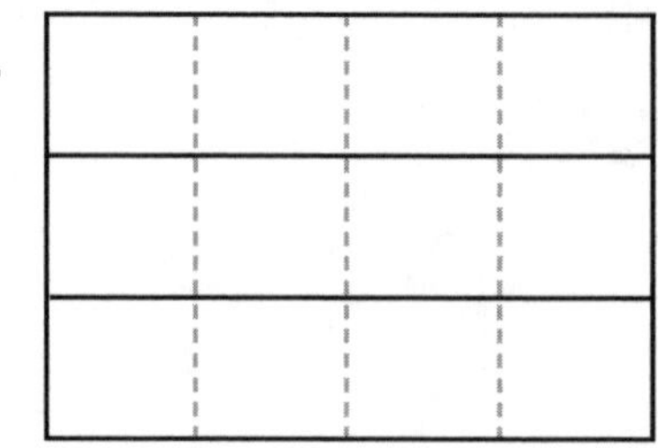

$\frac{1}{4}$ of $\frac{2}{3} =$

c.

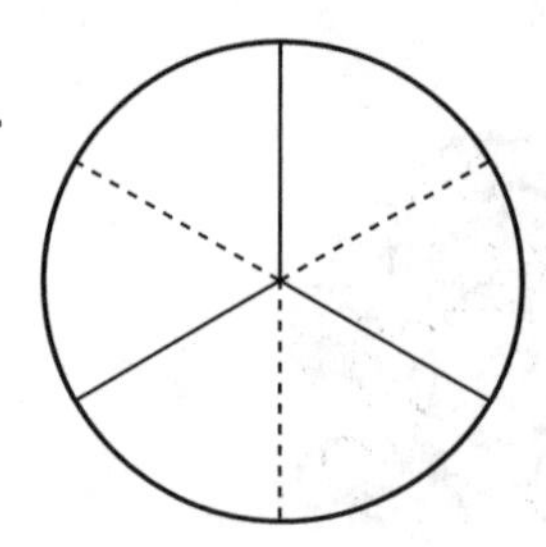

$\frac{1}{2}$ of $\frac{1}{3} =$

2.3 Multiply. Reduce answers to lowest terms.

a. $\frac{1}{4}$ of $\frac{2}{3}$ = $\frac{1}{6}$ of $\frac{3}{5}$ = $\frac{2}{5}$ of $\frac{5}{9}$ =

b. $\frac{3}{7} \times \frac{2}{3}$ = $\frac{1}{2} \times \frac{1}{4}$ = $\frac{4}{5} \times \frac{1}{3}$ =

c. $\frac{1}{8}$ of $\frac{1}{5}$ = $\frac{5}{6}$ of $\frac{1}{3}$ = $\frac{2}{7}$ of $\frac{3}{8}$ =

d. $\frac{3}{4} \times \frac{2}{3}$ = $\frac{5}{8} \times \frac{3}{4}$ = $\frac{5}{7} \times \frac{2}{5}$ =

2.4 Find the average. Add, count, divide.

a. 5, 6, 6, 7 __________ 3, 7, 14, 20 __________

b. 15, 22, 35 __________ 7, 13, 18, 23, 29 __________

2.5 Write the value of 8 in each number.

38,056 __________ 980,631 __________ 8,235,576 __________ 569,804 __________ 7,638 __________

2.6 Multiply. Remember the zero place holders.

$$\begin{array}{r} 3{,}826 \\ \times \quad 5 \\ \hline \end{array} \qquad \begin{array}{r} 2{,}763 \\ \times \quad 28 \\ \hline \end{array} \qquad \begin{array}{r} 5{,}904 \\ \times \quad 56 \\ \hline \end{array} \qquad \begin{array}{r} 7{,}321 \\ \times \quad 297 \\ \hline \end{array}$$

2.7 Divide. Remember the steps. (You may use short division.)
Divide. Multiply. Subtract. Compare. Bring down (or tuck in the number).

$7\overline{)280}$ $\qquad 5\overline{)354}$ $\qquad 6\overline{)87}$ $\qquad 8\overline{)360}$

Data is a list of facts from which a conclusion can be drawn.

A graph is a special kind of chart used to display the data.
A **picture graph** is similar to a bar graph. Pictures are used to show the data.

2.8 The picture graph shows the number of students in the 5th grade class that read five or more books each week during the month of January. Read the graph and then answer the questions.

Number of Books Read

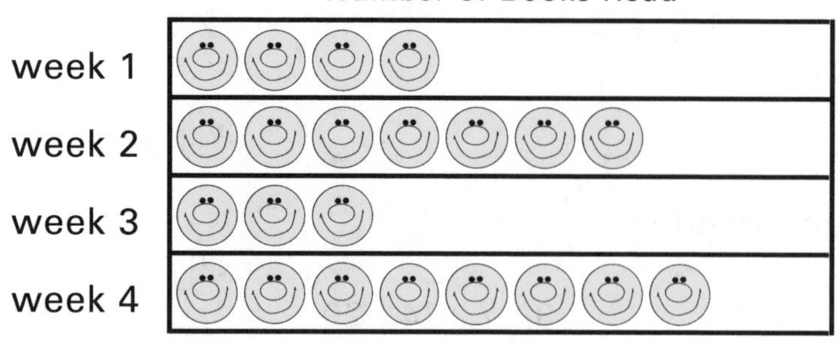

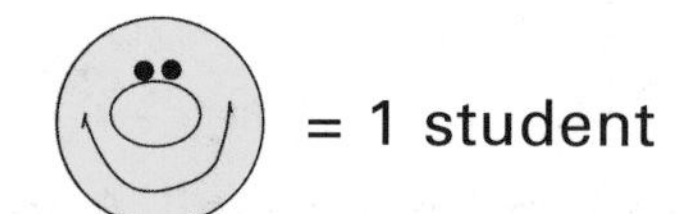

How many students read
five or more books during week 1? _______ 2? _______ 3? _______ 4? _______

2.9 Use the data to complete the picture graph.
There were 14 people in Sarah's youth group.

5 had blue eyes. 3 had brown eyes. 4 had green eyes. 2 had hazel eyes.

Eye Colors

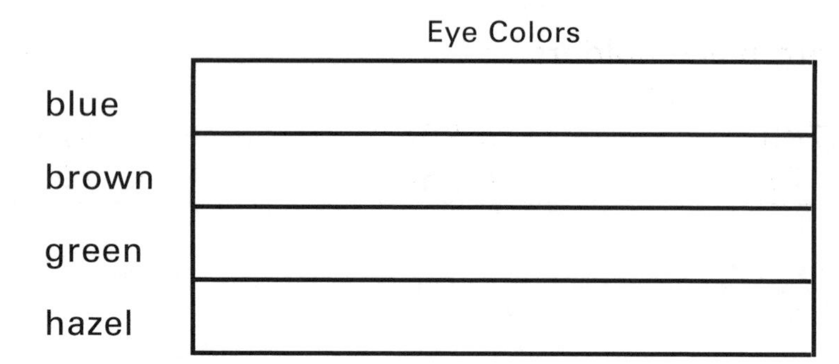

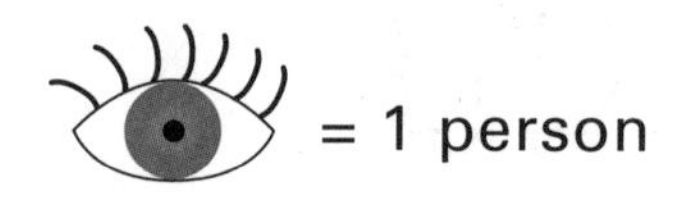

2.10 Numbers can be rounded to any place.
Find the place. Look at the first digit to the right.
Round to the nearest ...

10.	265 _______	3,874 _______	9,650 _______
100.	832 _______	7,350 _______	25,763 _______
1,000.	4,082 _______	56,367 _______	431,950 _______

Bar graphs and line graphs are drawn in the shape of rectangles. Follow the steps to complete each type of graph.

Average Life Expectancy in Years		
Grizzly Bear 25	Camel 12	Chipmunk 8
Elephant 35	Guinea Pig 4	Lion 15

1. Write the title at the top of the graph.
2. Decide on the information to show along the left side and bottom of the graph.
3. Decide the numbering system to use. (Count by 1's, 2's, 5's, or 10's.)
4. Draw the lines of the graph in the rectangle.
5. Post the data to the graph.

2.11 Complete the bar graph. Use your ruler! Be neat.

____

2.12 Complete the line graph. Use your ruler! Be neat.

____

When we cannot subtract a fraction, we borrow from the whole number.

$$\begin{array}{r} \overset{0}{\cancel{1}} = \frac{5}{5} \\ -\ \frac{3}{5} = \frac{3}{5} \\ \hline \frac{2}{5} \end{array} \qquad \begin{array}{r} \overset{6}{\cancel{7}}\frac{1}{8} + \frac{8}{8} = \frac{9}{8} \\ -\ 2\frac{6}{8} \quad\ \ = \frac{6}{8} \\ \hline 4 \qquad\qquad \frac{3}{8} \end{array}$$

Change the borrowed 1 to a fraction.

(Use the denominator already in the fraction.)

If there is a fraction in the minuend, add to it.

Rewrite the problem. Subtract.

Remember the whole number.

2.13 Subtract.

$$6 - \frac{2}{3} \qquad 9 - 1\frac{5}{8} \qquad 7\frac{1}{6} - 3\frac{5}{6} \qquad 5\frac{1}{4} - 2\frac{3}{4} \qquad 9\frac{3}{8} - 2\frac{7}{8}$$

When there are unlike denominators, find the common denominator.
Borrow if necessary. Circle the answer.

$$\begin{array}{r} \overset{5}{\cancel{6}}\frac{1}{5} = \frac{2}{10} + \frac{10}{10} = \frac{12}{10} \\ -\ 3\frac{3}{10} = \frac{3}{10} \qquad\qquad \frac{3}{10} \\ \hline 2\frac{9}{10} \qquad\qquad\qquad\qquad \frac{9}{10} \end{array}$$

Find a common denominator. (10)

Write equivalent fractions.

Borrow 1. $(\frac{10}{10})$ Add to $\frac{2}{10}$. $(\frac{12}{10})$

Subtract fractions and whole numbers.
Rewrite the fraction next to the whole number.

2.14 Subtract. Show each step. Circle answers.

a. $9\frac{1}{4} - 3\frac{5}{8}$ $\qquad 9\frac{2}{6} - 4\frac{2}{3}$ $\qquad 8\frac{4}{9} - 5\frac{5}{6}$ $\qquad 9\frac{3}{8} - 4\frac{3}{4}$

b. $12\frac{2}{9} - 7\frac{1}{3}$ $\qquad 8\frac{5}{12} - 6\frac{1}{2}$ $\qquad 7\frac{3}{5} - 1\frac{7}{10}$ $\qquad 5\frac{1}{4} - 3\frac{1}{3}$

Each type of measurement has units of measure that range from small to large.

2.15 Write what is being measured ... length, weight, dry volume, or liquid volume. Number each group in order from small to large.

a. ________ ______ quart ______ gallon ______ ounce ______ pint

b. ________ ______ peck ______ pint ______ quart ______ bushel

c. ________ ______ inches ______ yards ______ miles ______ feet

d. ________ ______ ton ______ ounce ______ pound

2.16 Tell the operation needed to solve the problem (multiply or divide). Circle the units of measurement. Solve the problem.

a. Jane needs 12 feet of ribbon for a pattern.
How many yards will she need to buy? __________ ______________

b. Jordan has a pitcher that contains 3 quarts of milk.
How many pints of milk are in the container? __________ ______________

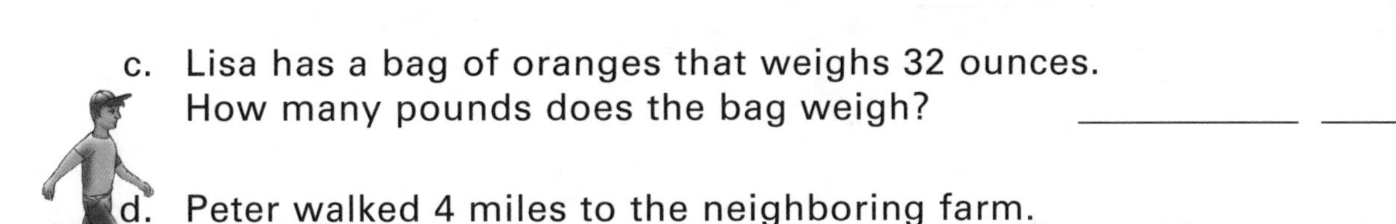

c. Lisa has a bag of oranges that weighs 32 ounces.
How many pounds does the bag weigh? __________ ______________

d. Peter walked 4 miles to the neighboring farm.
How many linear feet did Peter walk? __________ ______________

2.17 Add. Convert answers to lowest terms.

3 qt. 1 pt.	5 qt. 6 oz.	6 ft. 8 in.	7 lb. 9 oz.
+ 4 qt. 1 pt.	+ 3 qt. 10 oz.	+ 5 ft. 7 in.	+ 4 lb. 12 oz.

2.18 Subtract.

6 gal. 2 qt.	5 T. 1,600 lb.	7 bu. 3 pk.	9 yd. 32 in.
– 3 gal. 1 qt.	– 3 T. 500 lb.	– 2 bu. 1 pk.	– 2 yd. 14 in.

Self Test 2

2.01 Solve the problems in multiplication of fractions.
Color the part of the drawing that illustrates your answer. (4 points)

a. 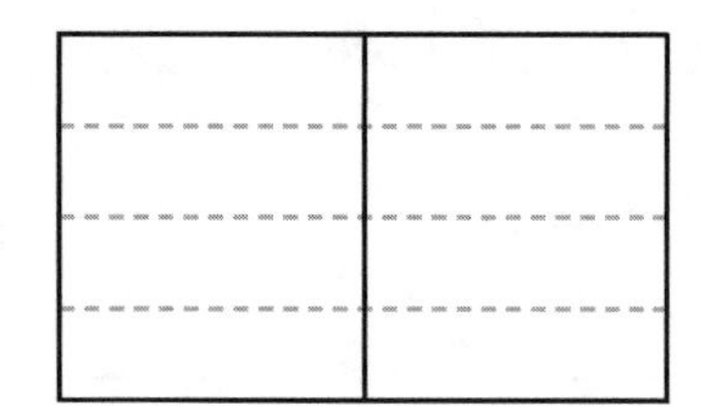

$\frac{3}{4}$ of $\frac{1}{2}$ =

b. 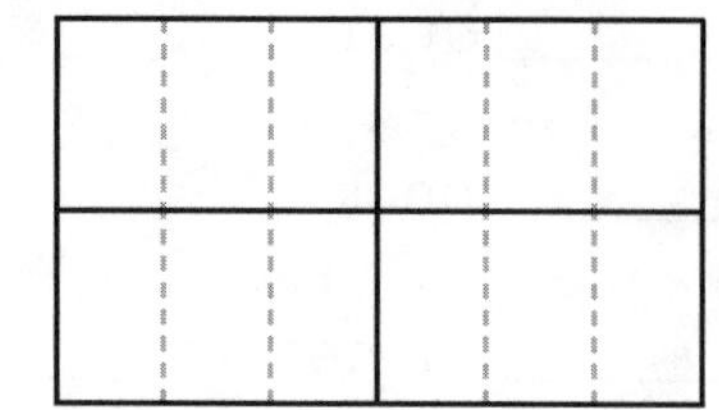

$\frac{2}{3}$ of $\frac{1}{4}$ =

2.02 Find the average. (each answer, 1 point)

11, 12, 16 ________

85, 9, 14, 28 ________

2.03 Multiply or divide. (each answer, 1 point)

$$\begin{array}{r} 2,408 \\ \times \quad 53 \\ \hline \end{array} \qquad \begin{array}{r} 706 \\ \times \ 183 \\ \hline \end{array} \qquad 6\overline{)240} \qquad 8\overline{)357}$$

2.04 Use the data to complete the picture graph. (3 points)

There were 18 people in the room. There were ...
4 men. 5 women. 7 boys. 2 girls.

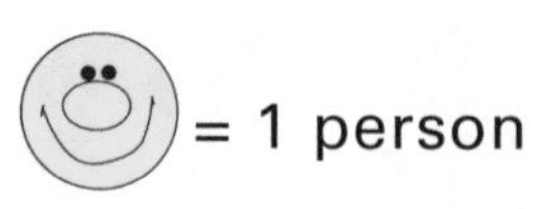
= 1 person

2.05 Round to the nearest ... (each answer, 1 point)

10. 7,635 ________ 100. 4,162 ________ 1,000. 8,965 ________

2.06 Subtract. (each answer, 1 point)

a. $2 - \frac{7}{8}$ ______ $6 - \frac{2}{7}$ ______ $8\frac{1}{5} - 4\frac{3}{5}$ ______ $4\frac{2}{9} - 1\frac{5}{9}$ ______

b. $7\frac{1}{4} - 3\frac{1}{2}$ ______ $9\frac{1}{3} - 5\frac{5}{6}$ ______ $5\frac{3}{10} - 2\frac{4}{5}$ ______ $6\frac{5}{12} - 4\frac{5}{6}$ ______

2.07 Write which group is being measured ...
length, weight, dry volume, or liquid volume.
Number each group in order from small to large. (4 points)

a. ________ ______ quart ______ pint ______ peck ______ bushel

b. ________ ______ feet ______ yards ______ inches ______ miles

2.08 Tell the operation needed to solve the problem (multiply or divide). Circle the units of measure. Solve the problem. each answer, 1 point)

Curt picked 8 pints of strawberries at the farm.
How many quarts did he pick? ____________ ______________

2.09 Add or subtract. Convert answers to lowest terms. (each answer, 1 point)

	5 ft. 8 in.
+	3 ft. 9 in.

	16 lb. 12 oz.
+	5 lb. 4 oz.

	5 gal. 3 qt.
–	1 gal. 2 qt.

My Score ____________
Teacher Check ____________

III. Part Three

Objectives

To multiply fractions
To review rounding, multi-digit numbers, patterns in addition and multiplication
To add and subtract decimals

3.1 Multiply. Simplify or reduce answers to lowest terms.

$\frac{3}{5} \times \frac{2}{3} =$ $\frac{5}{6} \times \frac{2}{10} =$ $\frac{4}{9} \times \frac{1}{2} =$ $\frac{3}{4} \times \frac{2}{6} =$

Some multiplication problems can be simplified before multiplying.
The fractions are simplified in the problem and then multiplied.
Find a common factor for one numerator and one denominator.

$\frac{5}{\not{6}_{2}} \times \frac{\not{3}^{1}}{4} = \frac{5}{8}$ 3 and 6 have a common factor of 3. Divide.
Multiply 5 x 1 and 2 x 4. The answer is in lowest terms.

3.2 Simplify in the problem. Multiply.

a. $\frac{6}{7} \times \frac{1}{3} =$ $\frac{2}{7} \times \frac{1}{8} =$ $\frac{7}{8} \times \frac{1}{14} =$ $\frac{5}{7} \times \frac{8}{15} =$

b. $\frac{1}{14} \times \frac{7}{8} =$ $\frac{5}{12} \times \frac{3}{4} =$ $\frac{14}{15} \times \frac{2}{7} =$ $\frac{5}{18} \times \frac{3}{8} =$

c. $\frac{3}{5} \times \frac{5}{11} =$ $\frac{2}{3} \times \frac{7}{8} =$ $\frac{4}{9} \times \frac{12}{13} =$ $\frac{1}{6} \times \frac{3}{5} =$

3.3 Joe's family has gone for a drive in the mountains. Follow the pattern. When will the drive up a mountain equal the drive down a mountain?

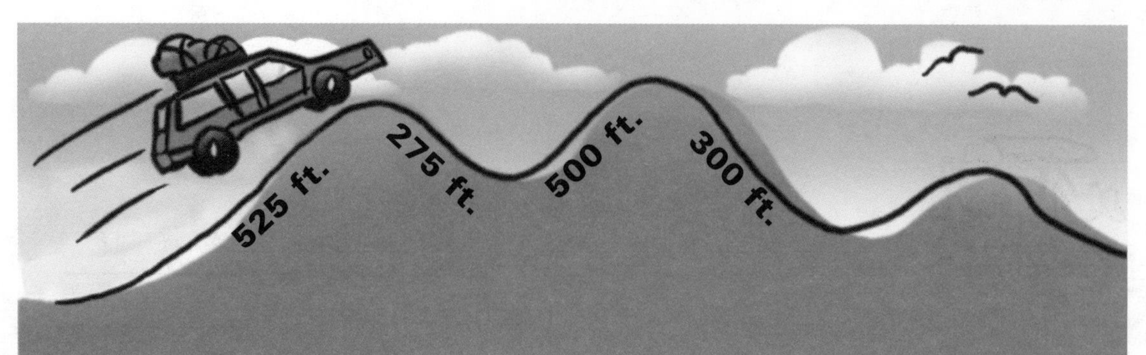

_______ feet

Rounding is a mathematical procedure that allows us to understand large numbers.

825,496,387 By the time the last digit is read, we lose the meaning of the value.

800,000,000 By rounding the number, the emphasis is placed on its value.

Numbers can be rounded to any place.
Locate the place. Find the digit to the right.
If the digit is 5 or more, round up. If the digit is 5 or less, round down.

Round to ten millions' place.	726,321,692	730,000,000
Round to hundred millions' place.	726,321,692	700,000,000

3.4 Round to the nearest ...

a. ten millions. 637,267,180 ____________ 751,436,429 ____________

b. hundred millions. 450,876,223 ____________ 921,830,546 ____________

3.5 The traffic in airports for one year is measured in number of passengers.

Atlanta 47,741,000 New York 26,796,036 Los Angeles 47,844,794
Houston 20,251,212 Honolulu 22,061,953 Chicago 65,091,168

a. Round each number to the nearest one millions.

Atlanta ____________ New York ____________ Los Angeles ____________

Houston ____________ Honolulu ____________ Chicago ____________

b. *About* how many passengers passed through all the airports? ____________

c. Which city served
the largest number of passengers? __________ the least number? __________

d. *About* how many more passengers
passed through New York than Honolulu? ________________

3.6 Write in number words.

763,052,193 ____

____

820,365,126 ____

____

Decimals are special fractions. The denominators are in a pattern of 10, 100, 1,000, ...

The place of the decimal point tells us the denominator of these special fractions.

units (whole numbers)			.	decimals (fractions)		
hundreds 100's	tens 10's	ones 1's	.	tenths 10ths	hundredths 100ths	thousandths 1,000ths

Decimals can be written as fractions or mixed numbers.

$.4 = \frac{4}{10}$ $.08 = \frac{8}{100}$ $.026 = \frac{26}{1,000}$ $53.79 = 53\frac{79}{100}$

3.7 Write each decimal as a fraction or mixed number.

.06 ______ .592 ______ 3.04 ______ 52.7 ______ 60.003 ______

Fractions or mixed numbers can be written as decimals.
Write the numerator as you would a whole number.
Count places from right to left for the denominator. Add zeros, if necessary.
Write the decimal point. Write the whole number.

$\frac{3}{100} = .03$ $\frac{87}{1,000} = .087$ $9\frac{2}{100} = 9.02$ $37\frac{15}{100} = 37.15$

3.8 Write each fraction or mixed number as a decimal.

$\frac{5}{100}$ ______ $\frac{72}{1,000}$ ______ $4\frac{2}{10}$ ______ $8\frac{15}{100}$ ______ $16\frac{4}{100}$ ______

Decimals that contain whole numbers are read as mixed numbers.

53.046 is fifty-three and forty-six thousandths.

3.9 Write decimals in words.

a. 4.05 ______________________ 52.3 ______________________

b. 3.071 ____

Decimal numbers are added or subtracted by lining the numbers in vertical columns by place value. We may carry or borrow as in whole numbers.

3.10 Add or subtract. Bring down the decimal point.

```
  76.57          8.05
  23.4          32.6          96.23        6.348
+ 47.369     +    .748      -  4.08      - 1.27
--------     --------       -------      ------
```

MATHEMATICS

506

LIFEPAC TEST

80/100

Name ____________________

Date ____________________

Score ____________________

MATHEMATICS 506: LIFEPAC TEST

1. Describe each number as ... (each answer, 1 point)

   a. proper fraction   b. improper fraction   c. mixed number

   $\frac{12}{7}$ __________ $6\frac{1}{3}$ __________ $\frac{15}{16}$ __________

2. Write in words. (each answer, 1 point)

   $\frac{3}{5}$ ______________________________ $8\frac{3}{7}$ ______________________________

3. Write the factors of 6 ____, ____, ____, ____ and 8. ____, ____, ____, ____

   What is the largest factor common to 6 and 8? _______ (3 points)

4. Write four multiples for 3 ____, ____, ____, ____ and 4. ____, ____, ____, ____

   Write the smallest multiple that 3 and 4 have in common. _______ (3 points)

5. Follow the steps to add or subtract fractions and mixed numbers. Find the common denominator. Reduce fractions to lowest terms. (each answer, 2 points)

   $6\frac{1}{4} + 3\frac{1}{3}$ $7\frac{8}{9} + 4\frac{2}{3}$ $8\frac{4}{5} - 3\frac{1}{10}$ $9\frac{1}{8} - 6\frac{3}{4}$

6. Write the formula for volume. (2 points)
   Find the volume for the rectangular solid in the illustration.

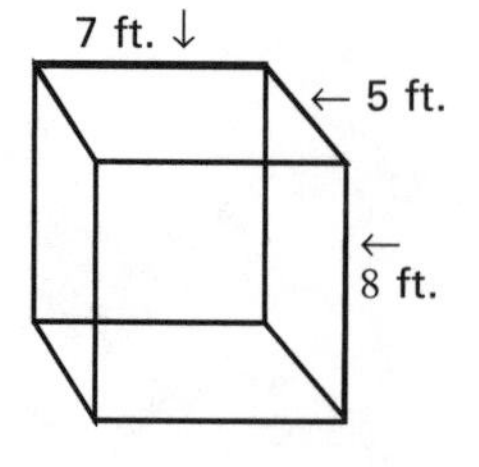

   V = _______ x _______ x _______

   V = ________________________

7. Round to the nearest 10,000. (each answer, 1 point)

   372,480 __________   45,328,638 __________   386,250,117 __________

8. Add. Convert answers to lowest terms. (each answer, 2 points)

9 wk. 5 da.		5 lb. 7 oz.		3 T. 1,630 lb.	
+ 7 wk. 8 da.		+ 4 lb. 15 oz.		+ 2 T. 573 lb.	

9. Use the data to complete the picture graph. (this problem, 4 points)

There were 24 animals at the pet show. There were ...

1 hamster 7 cats 6 fish 10 dogs

Title ______________________

________ = 1 animal

10. Simplify in the problem. Multiply. (each answer, 2 points)

$\frac{5}{8} \times \frac{4}{5} =$ $\frac{7}{10} \times \frac{5}{8} =$ $\frac{8}{9} \times \frac{3}{16} =$

11. Write numbers in words. (each answer, 1 point)

438,065,902 ____

____

19.063 ____

12. Add or subtract. (each answer, 2 points)

$$\begin{array}{r} 3.67 \\ 2.8 \\ +\ 4.003 \\ \hline \end{array} \qquad \begin{array}{r} 26.1 \\ 4.86 \\ +\ .045 \\ \hline \end{array} \qquad \begin{array}{r} 54.63 \\ -\ 29.75 \\ \hline \end{array} \qquad \begin{array}{r} 3.846 \\ -\ 2.59 \\ \hline \end{array}$$

13. Reorder and group the numbers. Add or multiply. (2 points each a. and b.)

a. $7 + 2 + 0 + 8 + 3 =$ ______________________ = __________

b. $1 \times 5 \times 9 \times 2 =$ ______________________ = __________

14. Triangles may be described by their sides or by their angles. (this problem, 6 pts)
Identify each triangle as ... (E) equilateral, (S) scalene, or (I) isosceles,
(R) right, (O) obtuse, or (A) acute.

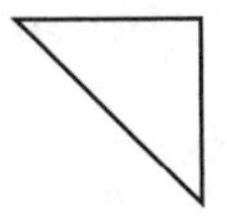

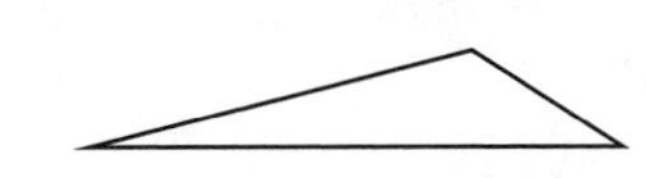

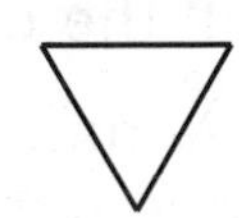

______ ______ ______ ______ ______ ______

15. Multiply or divide. (each answer, 2 points)

$$\begin{array}{r} 278 \\ \times\ 350 \\ \hline \end{array} \qquad \begin{array}{r} 5{,}934 \\ \times\ 63 \\ \hline \end{array} \qquad 6\overline{)414} \qquad 5\overline{)67}$$

16. Multiply. (each answer, 2 points)

$$\begin{array}{r} .45 \\ \times\ .3 \\ \hline \end{array} \qquad \begin{array}{r} .08 \\ \times\ .06 \\ \hline \end{array} \qquad \begin{array}{r} .04 \\ \times\ .7 \\ \hline \end{array} \qquad \begin{array}{r} .62 \\ \times\ .49 \\ \hline \end{array}$$

17. Circle the correct symbol. (each letter, 1 point)

a. $\frac{5}{9}$ (>, <) $\frac{3}{5}$ ________________ ________________

b. $\frac{7}{8}$ (>, <) $\frac{3}{4}$ ________________ ________________

18. Subtract. Remember to borrow. (each answer, 2 points)

$$\begin{array}{r} 5 \text{ yr. } 4 \text{ mo.} \\ -\ 2 \text{ yr. } 7 \text{ mo.} \\ \hline \end{array} \qquad \begin{array}{r} 9 \text{ ft. } 3 \text{ in.} \\ -\ 5 \text{ ft. } 8 \text{ in.} \\ \hline \end{array} \qquad \begin{array}{r} 8 \text{ qt. } 5 \text{ oz.} \\ -\ 3 \text{ qt. } 7 \text{ oz.} \\ \hline \end{array}$$

(4 points each question 19 - 22)

19. Corey earned $5 on Monday, $7 each on Tuesday and Wednesday, $3 on Thursday, and $6 each on Friday and Saturday. Altogether, he earned $34.

Express the paragraph as an equation. ____________________

20. Lori has read $\frac{5}{8}$ of the book. Kevin has read $\frac{2}{3}$ of the book.
Who has read more of the book? ____________

21. 7 of the 10 people in line wore red hats.
What is the ratio of red hats to the total number of people? ____________

22. Tell the operation needed to solve the problem. Solve. Label the answer.

Lisa had 27 feet of ribbon.
How many yards did she have? ____________ ____________

There are patterns in addition and multiplication that make it easier for us to solve problems. However, the rules must be followed, or the answers will be incorrect.

> Adding zero to a number does not change the number (answer).
> Multiplying by one does not change the number (answer).
> Multiplying by zero results in an answer of zero.

> Changing the order of numbers does not change the answer.
> Changing the grouping of numbers does not change the answer.

In the examples, numbers are grouped to achieve totals of tens' numbers. Then, the additional numbers (7, 4) are added. Zero is deleted.

$6 + 8 + 2 + 4 + 7 + 0 = 27$ $\qquad$ $(6 + 4) + (8 + 2) + 7 = 27$

$17 + 4 + 8 + 23 + 32 = 84$ $\qquad$ $(17 + 23) + (8 + 32) + 4 = 84$

3.11 Look for the zero first. It has no value. It may be deleted. Reorder and group the numbers. Add.

a. $3 + 5 + 7 + 6 + 5 =$ ______________________ = __________

b. $9 + 4 + 8 + 2 + 1 =$ ______________________ = __________

c. $15 + 37 + 0 + 5 + 13 =$ ______________________ = __________

d. $18 + 22 + 29 + 6 + 1 =$ ______________________ = __________

e. $31 + 14 + 19 + 13 + 6 =$ ______________________ = __________

The first example contains a zero. This immediately results in an answer of zero. The second example deletes 1 and regroups the numbers for easier multiplication.

$4 \times 8 \times 0 \times 5 = 0$

$9 \times 4 \times 2 \times 1 = 72$ $\qquad$ $9 \times (4 \times 2) = 72$

3.12 Look for the zero first. If there is no zero, go on to the next step. Reorder and group the numbers. Multiply.

a. $7 \times 2 \times 5 \times 1 =$ ______________________ = __________

b. $6 \times 1 \times 0 \times 4 =$ ______________________ = __________

c. $8 \times 6 \times 5 \times 1 =$ ______________________ = __________

d. $2 \times 4 \times 3 \times 5 =$ ______________________ = __________

e. $9 \times 1 \times 3 \times 2 =$ ______________________ = __________

3.13 Match.

a.	_______ right angle	1.	less than 90°
b.	_______ equilateral triangle	2.	two equal sides
c.	_______ isosceles triangle	3.	equal to 90°
d.	_______ obtuse angle	4.	no equal sides
e.	_______ scalene triangle	5.	greater than 90°
f.	_______ acute angle	6.	all sides equal

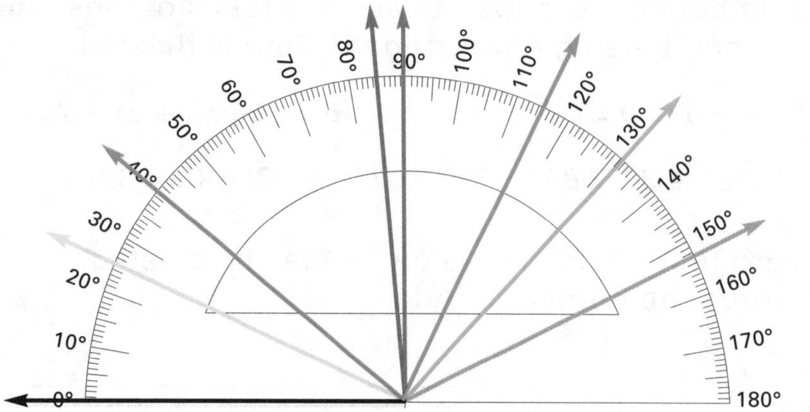

3.14 Measure the size of the angles in degrees.
Describe the angle as (A) acute, (R) right, or (O) obtuse.

The angle whose sides are ...

a. yellow and brown. ________ ______   red and brown. ________ ______

b. blue and pink. ________ ______   purple and brown. ________ ______

c. yellow and red. ________ ______   purple and green. ________ ______

3.15 Triangles may be described by their sides or by their angles.
Identify each triangle as ... (E) equilateral, (S) scalene, or (I) isosceles,
(R) right, (O) obtuse, or (A) acute.

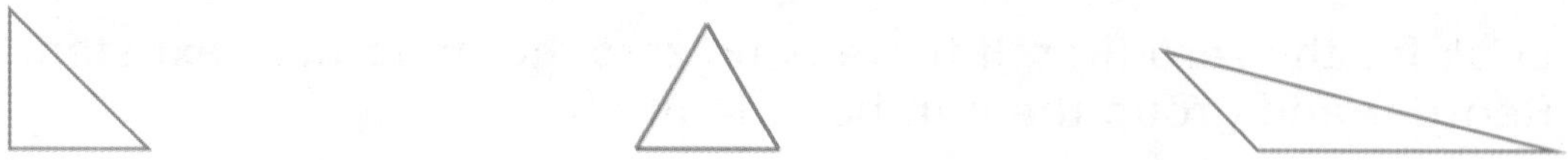

______ ______   ______ ______   ______ ______

3.16 Circle the triangle that is congruent to the first triangle.
Draw a line under the triangle that is similar.

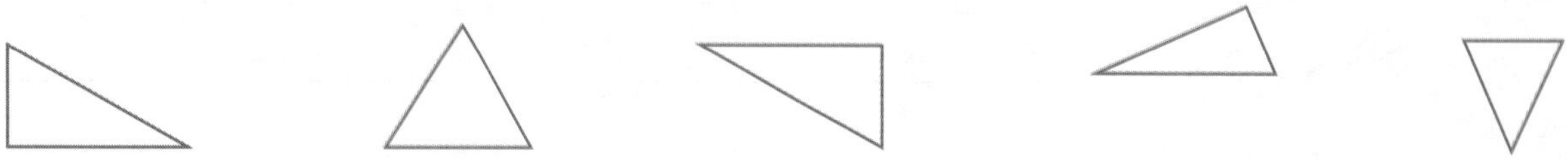

3.17 Multiply. Remember the zero place holders.

a.

$$\begin{array}{r} 476 \\ \times\ 38 \\ \hline \end{array} \qquad \begin{array}{r} 291 \\ \times\ 40 \\ \hline \end{array} \qquad \begin{array}{r} 805 \\ \times\ 76 \\ \hline \end{array} \qquad \begin{array}{r} 397 \\ \times\ 54 \\ \hline \end{array}$$

b.

$$\begin{array}{r} 3,853 \\ \times\ 47 \\ \hline \end{array} \qquad \begin{array}{r} 5,631 \\ \times\ 28 \\ \hline \end{array} \qquad \begin{array}{r} 3,207 \\ \times\ 50 \\ \hline \end{array} \qquad \begin{array}{r} 6,119 \\ \times\ 83 \\ \hline \end{array}$$

c.

$$\begin{array}{r} 672 \\ \times\ 320 \\ \hline \end{array} \qquad \begin{array}{r} 235 \\ \times\ 518 \\ \hline \end{array} \qquad \begin{array}{r} 703 \\ \times\ 284 \\ \hline \end{array} \qquad \begin{array}{r} 857 \\ \times\ 504 \\ \hline \end{array}$$

3.18 Divide. Remember the steps. (You may use short division.)
Divide. Multiply. Subtract. Compare. Bring down (or tuck in the number).

a.

$3\overline{)57}$ $\qquad$ $5\overline{)69}$ $\qquad$ $7\overline{)254}$ $\qquad$ $9\overline{)95}$

b.

$4\overline{)263}$ $\qquad$ $6\overline{)79}$ $\qquad$ $7\overline{)365}$ $\qquad$ $4\overline{)43}$

Self Test 3

3.01 Simplify in the problem. Multiply. (each answer, 1 point)

$\frac{3}{8} \times \frac{4}{5} =$ $\frac{1}{7} \times \frac{14}{15} =$ $\frac{6}{7} \times \frac{5}{12} =$

3.02 Round to the nearest ... (each answer, 1 point)

a. ten millions. 583,251,060 ____________ 937,446,504 ____________

b. hundred millions. 357,241,884 ____________ 105,263,917 ____________

3.03 Write in number words. (1 point)

805,361,294 ____

____

3.04 Write each decimal as a fraction or mixed number. (each answer, 1 point)

.5 ________ .041 ________ 5.16 ________ 21.3 ________

3.05 Write each fraction or mixed number as a decimal. (each answer, 1 point)

$\frac{6}{100}$ ________ $\frac{53}{1,000}$ ________ $4\frac{7}{10}$ ________ $18\frac{3}{1,000}$ ________

3.06 Write decimals in words. (each answer, 1 point)

9.8 ________________________ 3.42 ________________________

3.07 Add or subtract. (each answer, 1 point)

$$\begin{array}{r} 4.067 \\ 8.5 \\ +\ 2.13 \\ \hline \end{array} \qquad \begin{array}{r} 31.24 \\ 5.103 \\ +\ 16.03 \\ \hline \end{array} \qquad \begin{array}{r} 41.54 \\ -\ 13.02 \\ \hline \end{array} \qquad \begin{array}{r} 2.675 \\ -\ 1.23 \\ \hline \end{array}$$

3.08 Reorder and group the numbers. Add or multiply. (8 points)

a. 2 + 5 + 0 + 5 + 8 = ________________________ = __________

b. 18 + 4 + 2 + 3 + 7 = ________________________ = __________

c. 6 x 3 x 2 x 1 = ________________________ = __________

d. 4 x 0 x 5 x 2 = ________________________ = __________

(each answer, 1 point)

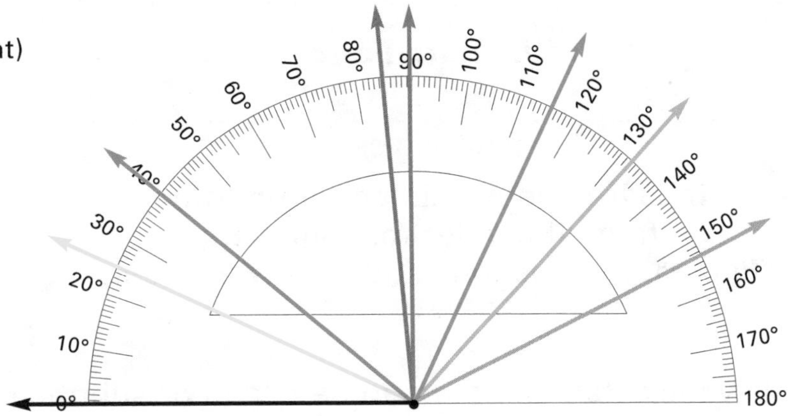

3.09 Measure the size of the angles in degrees.
Describe the angle as (A) acute, (R) right, or (O) obtuse.

The angle whose sides are ...

a. yellow and red. ________ _____ green and red. ________ _____

b. yellow and brown. ________ _____ red and pink. ________ _____

3.010 Triangles may be described by their sides or by their angles.
Identify each triangle as ... (E) equilateral, (S) scalene, or (I) isosceles,
(R) right, (O) obtuse, or (A) acute.

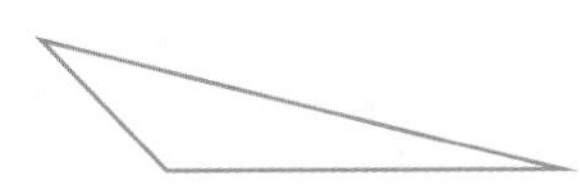

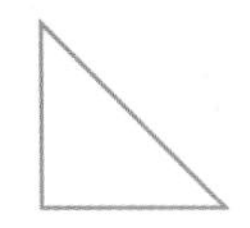

______ ______ ______ ______ ______ ______

3.011 Circle the rectangle that is congruent to the first rectangle.
Draw a line under the rectangle that is similar.

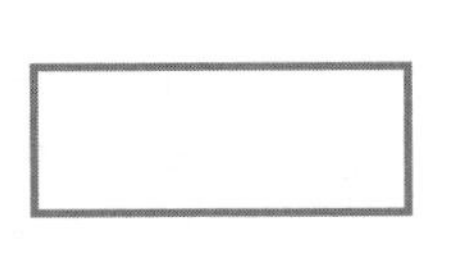
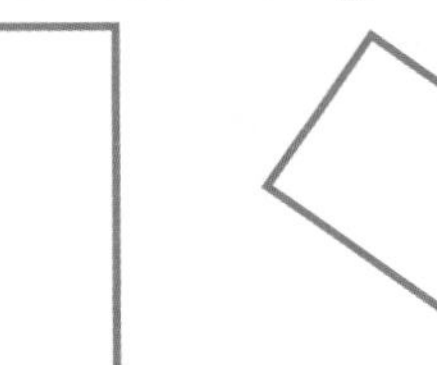

3.012 Multiply or divide.

$$\begin{array}{r} 432 \\ \times\ 260 \\ \hline \end{array} \qquad \begin{array}{r} 5{,}618 \\ \times\ 54 \\ \hline \end{array} \qquad 8\overline{)720} \qquad 5\overline{)51}$$

My Score ________

Teacher Check ________

IV. Part Four

Objectives

To learn about ratio and proportion
To multiply decimal numbers
To compare fractions and review formulas

4.1 Fractions must have like denominators to be added or subtracted. Answers should be simplified or reduced to lowest terms.

a. $\frac{2}{3} + \frac{4}{5}$ $\qquad$ $\frac{5}{9} + \frac{2}{6}$ $\qquad$ $\frac{1}{2} + \frac{2}{3}$ $\qquad$ $\frac{4}{7} + \frac{3}{14}$

b. $\frac{7}{8} - \frac{3}{6}$ $\qquad$ $\frac{3}{5} - \frac{1}{3}$ $\qquad$ $\frac{3}{4} - \frac{2}{3}$ $\qquad$ $\frac{11}{12} - \frac{5}{6}$

4.2 Fractions do not need like denominators to be multiplied. Simplify in the problem before multiplying.

a. $\frac{4}{9} \times \frac{3}{5} =$ $\qquad$ $\frac{7}{8} \times \frac{4}{9} =$ $\qquad$ $\frac{4}{5} \times \frac{1}{2} =$ $\qquad$ $\frac{5}{9} \times \frac{3}{8} =$

b. $\frac{6}{7} \times \frac{1}{12} =$ $\qquad$ $\frac{2}{5} \times \frac{15}{16} =$ $\qquad$ $\frac{3}{7} \times \frac{7}{9} =$ $\qquad$ $\frac{2}{3} \times \frac{9}{10} =$

4.3 Write the equivalent fraction on the line.

$\frac{15}{24}$ $\qquad$ $\frac{9}{12}$ $\qquad$ $\frac{8}{18}$ $\qquad$ $\frac{8}{20}$ $\qquad$ $\frac{4}{6}$ $\qquad$ $\frac{10}{12}$

$\frac{2}{3} =$ ______ $\qquad$ $\frac{4}{9} =$ ______ $\qquad$ $\frac{2}{5} =$ ______ $\qquad$ $\frac{5}{8} =$ ______ $\qquad$ $\frac{3}{4} =$ ______ $\qquad$ $\frac{5}{6} =$ ______

Ratio or proportion expresses a relationship between two numbers.

The numbers are usually written as fractions. Fractions with the same ratios are equivalent fractions. We can express ratios in several ways.

We write ...	We say ...
$\frac{2}{3} = \frac{4}{6}$	Two-thirds equals four-sixths.
2:3 = 4:6	Two is to three as four is to six.

There are 3 people in a room. 2 of the people are boys.

We say that $\frac{2}{3}$ of the people in the room are boys.

Suppose the ratio of boys stays the same as the size of the group increases.

If the group increases to 6 people, how many are boys?

We solve the problem by writing equivalent fractions.

The denominators represent the whole of the groups.

The numerators represent the part we are talking about.

$\frac{2}{3}$ $\frac{\text{boys in first group}}{\text{people in first group}}$ $\frac{?}{6}$ $\frac{\text{boys in second group}}{\text{people in second group}}$

We solve for equivalent fractions by dividing and multiplying. 6 ÷ 3 x 2 = 4

If there are 6 people in a room, 4 will be boys.

4.4 Using the ratio 2:3, how many boys would there be in a group of

9? ________ 12? ________ 18? ________ 27? ________

4.5 Judy was setting the table for a picnic. She only had 5 paper plates. 3 of the plates were green. If she wanted to keep the same ratio of green plates to the total number of plates, how many green plates would she need altogether to serve 15 people? ____________

4.6 Benny had 8 coins in his pocket. 5 of the coins were pennies. Andrew had 16 coins in his pocket. He had the same ratio of pennies that Benny had. How many pennies did Andrew have in his pocket? ____________

When multiplying by a number in the sequence of 10, 100, and 1,000, count the number of zeros in the multiplier and add them to the multiplicand.

53 x 10 = 530 53 x 100 = 5,300 53 x 1,000 = 53,000

4.7 Multiply. Remember to write the comma in your answer.

a. 10 x 35 = ____________ 100 x 470 = ____________

b. 10 x 10 = ____________ 10 x 100 = ____________

c. 100 x 100 = ____________ 100 x 1,000 = ____________

4.8 Multiply. *Do not reduce or simplify.*

$\frac{3}{10} \times \frac{4}{10} =$ ________ $\frac{3}{10} \times \frac{14}{100} =$ ________ $\frac{7}{100} \times \frac{15}{100} =$ ________

Each problem in ex. 4.8 can be written as a problem in multiplication of decimals.
The problem will resemble a problem in multiplication of whole numbers.
The decimal points do not need to be lined up as in addition and subtraction.

```
   .4
 x .3
 ----
  .12
```

Multiply. 3 x 4 = 12 Write the answer. Count decimal places.
.4 has one place. .3 has one place. There are two altogether.
Starting from the right and counting to the left, count two decimal places in the answer. Write the decimal point.
Compare to your answer in the first problem in ex. 4.8.

4.9 Write the answer in the blanks.

Multiply. 3 x 14 = 42 Count decimal places in the problem.

```
  .14
 x .3
 ----
   42
```

.14 has ______ places. .3 has ______ place. There are _____ altogether.

Working from right to left, count _____ decimal places in the answer.

Add zeros place holders, if necessary. Write the decimal point.
Compare to your answer in the second problem in ex. 4.8.

4.10 Write the answers on the lines.

Multiply. 7 x 15 = ________ Count decimal places in the problem.

```
  .15
 x .07
 -----
```

.15 has ______ places. .07 has ______ places. There are ______ altogether.

Working from right to left, count _____ decimal places in the answer.

Add zeros place holders if necessary. Write the decimal point.
Compare to your answer in the third problem in ex. 4.8.

4.11 Multiply as whole numbers. Count decimal places in the problem.
Add zero place holders, if necessary. Write the decimal.

```
  .35      .63      .47      .59      .08
 x .4    x .08    x .21    x  .2    x .06
 ----    -----    -----    -----    -----
```

An equation is a number sentence that contains an equal sign.

Certain equations are called formulas.
We can substitute numbers in the formula to solve a problem.
Formulas should be memorized so they are always available when we need them.

Perimeter = 2 x length + 2 x width   Area = length x width

Decide on the correct formula. Use N for the missing number.
Clear the numbers from the side of the equation that contains the N.
The same operation must be used on both sides of the equation.

4.12 Write the answers on the blanks.

a. The area of the room is 72 square feet. The length is 9 feet. What is the width of the room?

$A = L \times W$	Write the formula. Substitute.
$72 = 9 \times N$	Write N for the missing number.
$72 \div 9 = 9 \times N \div 9$	Clear 9 from the equation.
____ feet = N (width)	Write the answer.

b. The room has a perimeter of 44 feet and a length of 12 feet. What is the width of the room?

$P = (2 \times L) + (2 \times W)$	Write the formula. Substitute.
$44 = (2 \times 12) + (2 \times N)$	Write N for the missing number.
$44 = 24 + 2\ N$	Complete the multiplication.
$44 - 24 = 24 + 2\ N - 24$	Clear 24 from the equation.
$20 \div 2 = 2N \div 2$	Clear 2 from the equation.
____ feet = N (width)	Write the answer.

4.13 Find the ...

a. A = 48 sq. ft.
L = 8 ft.   W = ?

b. A = 63 sq. ft.
W = 7 ft.   L = ?

c. P = 56 ft.
L = 16 ft.   W = ?

d. P = 52 ft.
W = 12 ft.   L = ?

▲ We use cross multiplication to solve for equivalent fractions.

$\frac{2}{3}$ (=, ≠) $\frac{6}{9}$ (= circled)

$2 \times 9 = 18$ Multiply opposite numerators and denominators.

$6 \times 3 = 18$ If the products are the same, the fractions are equal.

4.14 Multiply. Circle the correct symbol.

a. $\frac{3}{5}$ (=, ≠) $\frac{6}{8}$ __________ __________

b. $\frac{4}{7}$ (=, ≠) $\frac{8}{14}$ __________ __________

c. $\frac{2}{3}$ (=, ≠) $\frac{12}{18}$ __________ __________

d. $\frac{7}{8}$ (=, ≠) $\frac{9}{15}$ __________ __________

■ We can use cross multiplication to find the larger fraction.

$\frac{2}{3}$ (>, <) $\frac{7}{9}$ (< circled)

$2 \times 9 = 18$ Multiply opposite numerators and denominators.

$7 \times 3 = 21$ The numerator that produces the larger product

$2 \times 9 < 7 \times 3$ is the numerator of the larger fraction.

4.15 Multiply. Circle the correct symbol.

a. $\frac{5}{8}$ (>, <) $\frac{2}{3}$ __________ __________

b. $\frac{1}{2}$ (>, <) $\frac{4}{9}$ __________ __________

c. $\frac{3}{8}$ (>, <) $\frac{3}{5}$ __________ __________

d. $\frac{3}{7}$ (>, <) $\frac{4}{8}$ __________ __________

e. $\frac{8}{9}$ (>, <) $\frac{5}{6}$ __________ __________

f. $\frac{15}{16}$ (>, <) $\frac{3}{4}$ __________ __________

4.16 Jordan had completed $\frac{4}{5}$ of his history assignment. Kevin had completed $\frac{2}{3}$ of his history assignment. Who had completed the greater part of his history assignment? __________

4.17 Melanie had completed $\frac{7}{8}$ of her library goal. Corrie had complete $\frac{9}{10}$ of her library goal. Who was closer to completing her library goal? __________

We can borrow when subtracting units of measurements.

$\begin{array}{r} \overset{4}{\cancel{5}} \text{ feet } \overset{16}{\cancel{4}} \text{ inches} \\ -\ 2 \text{ feet } 9 \text{ inches} \\ \hline 2 \text{ feet } 7 \text{ inches} \end{array}$	We cannot subtract 9 inches from 4 inches. We borrow 1 foot. Change 5 feet to 4 feet. 1 foot = 12 inches Add. 12 + 4 = 16 inches Subtract. 16 – 9 = 7 inches 4 – 2 = 2 feet

4.18 Subtract.

$\begin{array}{r} 5 \text{ lb. } 2 \text{ oz.} \\ -\ 3 \text{ lb. } 9 \text{ oz.} \\ \hline \end{array}$ $\begin{array}{r} 14 \text{ yd. } 1 \text{ ft.} \\ -\ 10 \text{ yd. } 2 \text{ ft.} \\ \hline \end{array}$ $\begin{array}{r} 3 \text{ mi. } 1{,}420 \text{ ft.} \\ -\ 1 \text{ mi. } 2{,}360 \text{ ft.} \\ \hline \end{array}$

$\begin{array}{r} 6 \text{ gal. } 1 \text{ qt.} \\ -\ 2 \text{ gal. } 2 \text{ qt.} \\ \hline \end{array}$ $\begin{array}{r} 3 \text{ pt. } 0 \text{ oz.} \\ -\ 1 \text{ pt. } 12 \text{ oz.} \\ \hline \end{array}$ $\begin{array}{r} 8 \text{ ft. } 6 \text{ in.} \\ -\ 2 \text{ ft. } 8 \text{ in.} \\ \hline \end{array}$

$\begin{array}{r} 15 \text{ bu. } 1 \text{ pk.} \\ -\ 4 \text{ bu. } 3 \text{ pk.} \\ \hline \end{array}$ $\begin{array}{r} 16 \text{ ft. } 2 \text{ in.} \\ -\ 12 \text{ ft. } 8 \text{ in.} \\ \hline \end{array}$ $\begin{array}{r} 7 \text{ qt. } 0 \text{ pt.} \\ -\ 2 \text{ qt. } 1 \text{ pt.} \\ \hline \end{array}$

4.19 Josie has a 3 gallon fish tank. She has a pitcher that contains 1 gallon and 1 quart of water. How much more water does she need to be able to fill the tank? __________

4.20 The Pattersons were pouring concrete for their driveway. They had completed 6 yards and 2 feet. The driveway was 10 yards long. How many more yards did they need to go to complete the driveway? __________

4.21 Multiply each number by 6.

5 ____ 3 ____ 10 ____ 7 ____ 4 ____ 0 ____ 9 ____ 6 ____

4.22 Divide each number by 8.

64 ____ 32 ____ 48 ____ 72 ____ 56 ____ 16 ____ 24 ____ 40 ____

Self Test 4

4.01 Add. Simplify or reduce to lowest terms. (each answer, 1 point)

$$\frac{1}{2} + \frac{2}{3} \qquad \frac{6}{10} + \frac{2}{5} \qquad \frac{3}{5} - \frac{1}{10} \qquad \frac{5}{6} - \frac{2}{3}$$

4.02 Multiply. Simplify in the problem. (each answer, 1 point)

$\frac{3}{7} \times \frac{14}{15} =$ $\frac{5}{8} \times \frac{7}{10} =$ $\frac{7}{15} \times \frac{3}{4} =$

4.03 Jorge has a box of 5 crayons. 3 of the crayons are green. What is the ratio of green crayons to the total number of crayons? (1 point) ____________

Steven has a box of 10 crayons. He has the same ratio of green crayons. How many green crayons does Steven have? (1 point) ____________

4.04 Multiply. Remember to write the comma in your answer. (each answer, 1 point)

a. 10 x 46 = ______________ 100 x 271 = ______________

b. 10 x 10 = ______________ 10 x 100 = ______________

4.05 Multiply. *Do not reduce or simplify.* (each answer, 1 point)

$\frac{2}{10} \times \frac{6}{10} =$ $\frac{5}{10} \times \frac{21}{100} =$ $\frac{8}{100} \times \frac{33}{100} =$

4.06 Multiply. Remember to write the decimal in the answer. (each answer, 1 point)

$$.53 \times .6 \qquad .03 \times .4 \qquad .09 \times .07 \qquad .45 \times .23$$

4.07 Use the formulas. Find the missing number. (each problem, 1 point)

a. A = 72 sq. ft. L = 9 ft. W = ?

b. P = 42 ft. L = 12 ft. W = ?

width ____________________

width ________________

4.08 Multiply. Circle the correct symbol. (each letter, 1 point)

a. $\frac{2}{3}$ (>, =, <) $\frac{5}{8}$ ____________________ ____________________

b. $\frac{3}{4}$ (>, =, <) $\frac{9}{12}$ ____________________ ____________________

c. $\frac{3}{8}$ (>, =, <) $\frac{1}{3}$ ____________________ ____________________

d. $\frac{5}{7}$ (>, =, <) $\frac{3}{4}$ ____________________ ____________________

4.09 Matthew has mowed $\frac{4}{5}$ of his yard. Mark has mowed $\frac{3}{4}$ of his yard. Which one is closer to completing his mowing? (1 point) ______________________

4.010 Subtract. (each answer, 1 point)

4 lb. 5 oz.	12 ft. 3 in.	9 hr. 18 min.
– 2 lb. 8 oz.	– 7 ft. 9 in.	– 2 hr. 40 min.

4.011 Lisa has mixed 2 gallons and 1 quart of juice for the party. She needs 5 gallons altogether. How much more juice does she need to mix for the party? (1 point) ______________________

25/31

My Score ______________

Teacher Check ______________

V. Part Five

Objectives

To read and write about the things I have learned

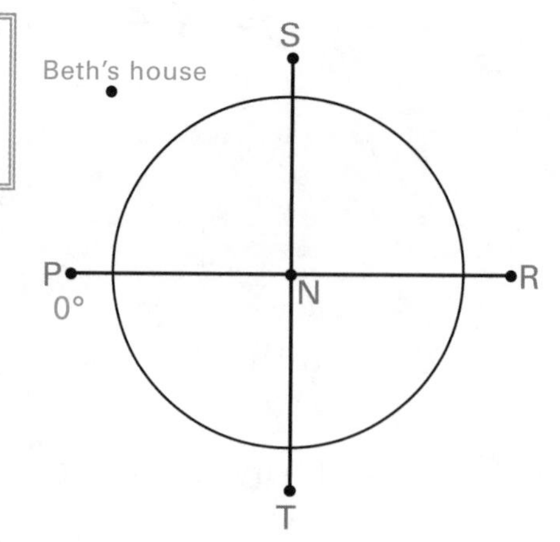

5.1 Joey and his classmates, Erica, Beth, and Chad, have gone on a field trip to the North Pole.
The students have made a map and marked the North Pole with the letter N.
They have drawn two lines, ST and PR on the map.
Point P has been marked 0°.

a. Joey is standing directly on the North Pole. If he turns around in a complete circle, how many degrees will that be? ____________

b. What is the relationship of lines ST and PR? ____________

Joey is facing 0° as he stands at the North Pole.

c. What degree is Joey facing if he turns and looks toward point S? ____________

d. How would you describe the angle PNS? ____________

e. What is point N to the angle PNS? ____________

Erica is standing at point R and Chad is standing at point T.

f. As Joey turns to face each one, write the number of degrees he has turned from point P. Erica ____________ Chad ____________

Find a point on the circle an equal distance between P and S.
Mark the point H. Draw a line between points N and H.

g. What is the measurement of angle PNH? ____________

Beth said that she could walk directly to her home if she continued in the direction of line NH.

h. If Beth walks 50 feet, will the size of angle PNH change? ____________

If Beth walks 50 miles, will the size of angle PNH change? ____________

If Beth always knows the location of points P and N, what degree angle can she follow to find her way home? ____________

Formulas may be difficult to use for the perimeter and area of irregular polygons.

A drawing can be made to scale
showing the size of the polygon in inches, feet, or yards.
Lines are drawn in the polygon to show the number of linear and square units.
The perimeter and area can then be measured by counting.

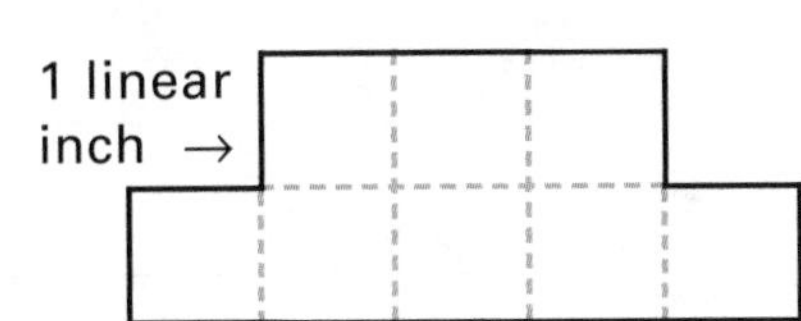

perimeter = 14 linear inches

area = 8 square inches

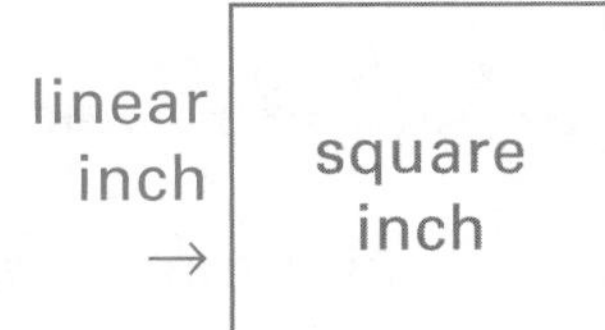

5.2 Each irregular polygon shows one linear or square measurement.
Use a ruler to draw lines showing the square units.
Use the counting method to find the perimeter and area. Label answers.

a.

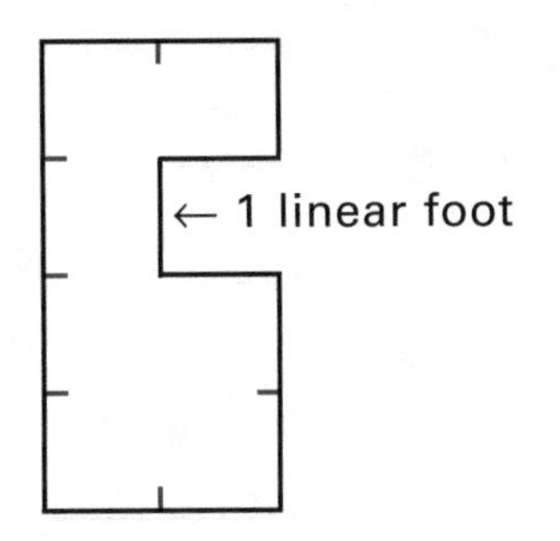

perimeter ______________________

area ______________________

b.

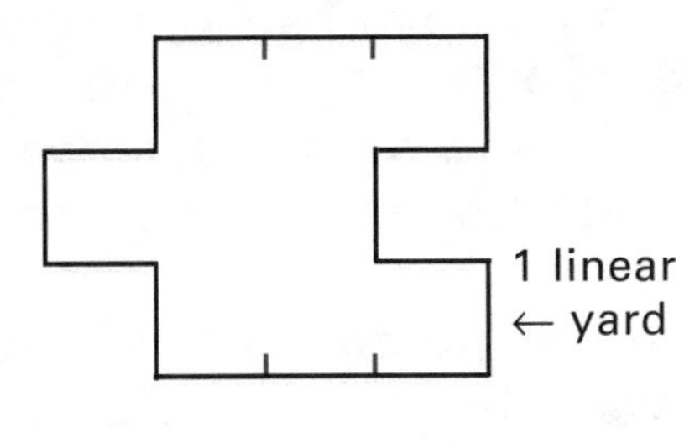

perimeter ______________________

area ______________________

c.

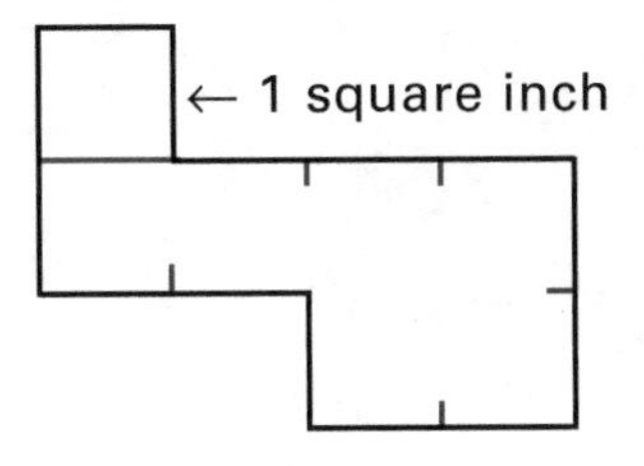

perimeter ______________________

area ______________________

d.

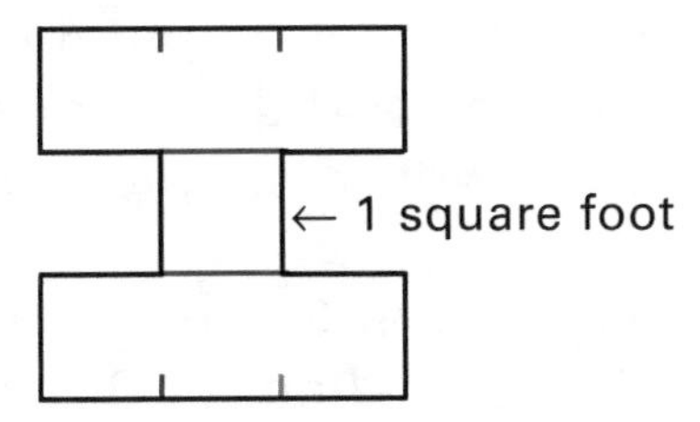

perimeter ______________________

area ______________________

5.3 Write what should be measured ... perimeter or area.

carpet a house ______________________

paint a ceiling ______________________

fence a yard ______________________

frame a picture ______________________

pour a concrete patio ______________________

chase the dog around the block ______________________

5.4 Answer the questions.

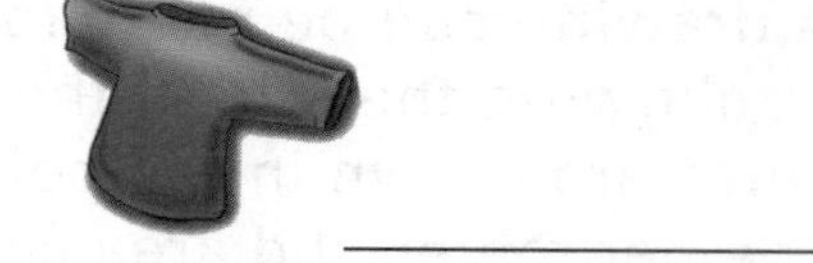

a. Jason is 15. Daniel is four years older than Jason. Ryan is eleven years younger than Daniel. What is their average age? ______

b. Add $\frac{2}{6}$ to $\frac{3}{6}$ and multiply by $\frac{1}{5}$. ______

c. Find the minuend. $? - 136 = 294$ ______

d. Find the missing addend. $26 + 45 + 32 + ? = 118$ ______

e. If you add $43 + 65 + 52$ will your answer be even or odd? ______

f. On the first day of school 6 boys wore blue shirts, 5 boys wore red shirts, 3 boys wore white shirts, and 1 boy wore a yellow shirt. What was the ratio of boys wearing blue shirts to the total number of boys? ______

On the second day of school, the boy wearing the yellow shirt was absent. How did that change the ratio of boys wearing blue shirts to the total number of boys? ______

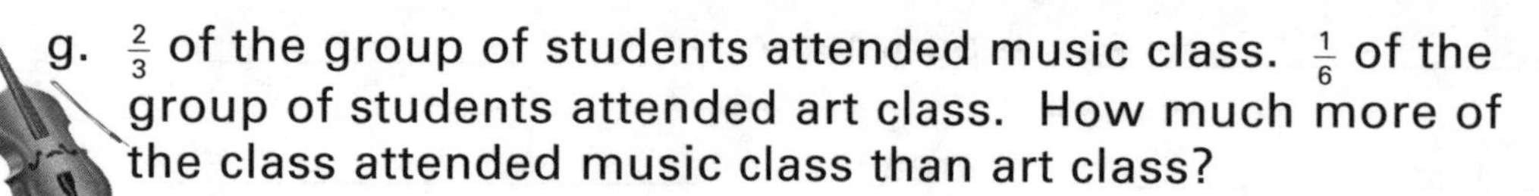

g. $\frac{2}{3}$ of the group of students attended music class. $\frac{1}{6}$ of the group of students attended art class. How much more of the class attended music class than art class? ______

h Andrew fed his dog 9 ounces of dog food each day. How much dog food did he need for a week's supply? Write your answer in simplest terms. ______

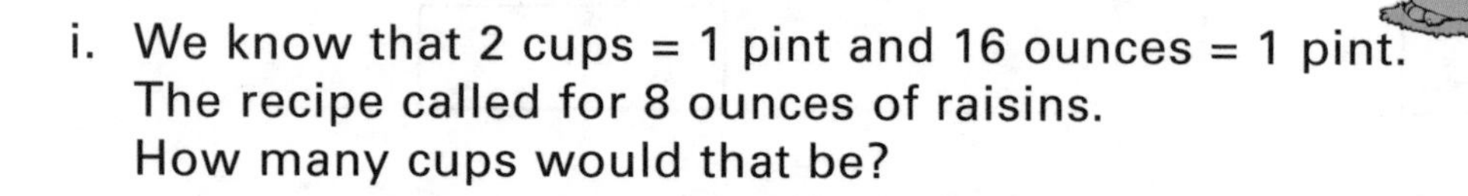

i. We know that 2 cups = 1 pint and 16 ounces = 1 pint. The recipe called for 8 ounces of raisins. How many cups would that be? ______

j. Andre walked $\frac{5}{6}$ of a mile on Monday, $\frac{6}{8}$ of a mile on Tuesday, and $\frac{2}{3}$ of a mile on Wednesday. On which day did he walk the farthest? ______

k. Stephanie borrowed ten dollars from her mother. On Friday, she paid back three dollars, two quarters, and three nickels. The following Friday, she paid back four dollars, six dimes, and nine pennies. How much does Stephanie still owe her mother? ______

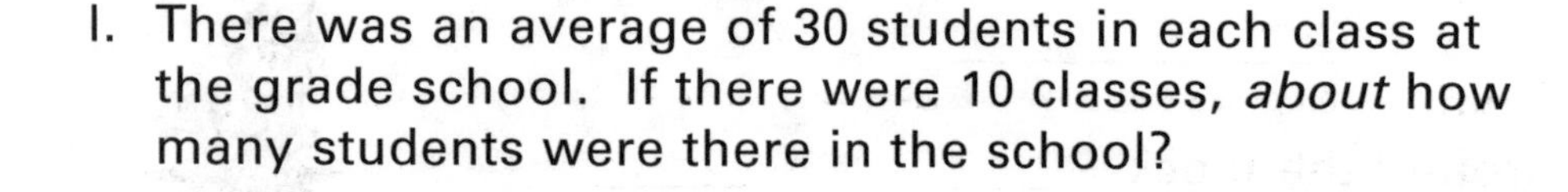

l. There was an average of 30 students in each class at the grade school. If there were 10 classes, *about* how many students were there in the school? ______

5.5 Answer the questions.

a. There were 56 cars in the freight train. If each car carried 100 boxes, how many boxes were there in the train? ____________

b. Subtract $\frac{1}{5}$ from $\frac{3}{5}$ and add $\frac{7}{10}$. ____________

c. Kevin's dad drives a truck route 270 miles per day. On Monday, it took him 6 hours to complete his route. On Tuesday, it took him 5 hours to complete his route.

How fast was he driving on Monday? ____________ on Tuesday? ____________

d. Denise was saving dimes. If she were able to save 8 dimes per week, how long would it take her to save 112 dimes? ____________

e. What is the difference between 12,367 and 8,471? ____________

f. Today is Wednesday, June 3. Jennifer's birthday is in 47 days. What is the day and date of Jennifer's birthday? ____________

g. Jason lost his watch while he and his brother were chasing each other around the outside of their house. Jason walked around the house three times before he found his watch. He told his mother that he had walked 432 feet looking for the watch. What is the perimeter of Jason's house? ____________

h. Show three ways to write 24 divided by 8. ________ ________ ________

i. Jeremy read twelve pages in his book on Friday, eighteen pages on Saturday, twenty on Sunday, and seven on Monday. Altogether, he read fifty-seven pages.

Express the paragraph as an equation. ____________________

j. Mary had divided the pie into three pieces so that each member of her family could have an equal amount. Mary decided to share one-half of her piece with her friend Josie. What is one-half of one-third? ____________

k. Add the problems. Write answers in Arabic numerals.

LXVII + XXXII = ____________ CCIX – CLIV = ____________

l. The state of Alaska has an area of 656,424 square miles. The state of Texas has an area of 266,807 square miles. *About* how much larger is Alaska than Texas? Express your answer to the nearest hundred thousand. ____________

5.6 Multiply. Remember the zero place holders.

a. 253 x 27   605 x 64   428 x 30   795 x 49

$$\begin{array}{r}253\\ \times\ 27\\ \hline\end{array}\qquad \begin{array}{r}605\\ \times\ 64\\ \hline\end{array}\qquad \begin{array}{r}428\\ \times\ 30\\ \hline\end{array}\qquad \begin{array}{r}795\\ \times\ 49\\ \hline\end{array}$$

b.

$$\begin{array}{r}567\\ \times\ 305\\ \hline\end{array}\qquad \begin{array}{r}900\\ \times\ 423\\ \hline\end{array}\qquad \begin{array}{r}2{,}356\\ \times\ 47\\ \hline\end{array}\qquad \begin{array}{r}9{,}456\\ \times\ 78\\ \hline\end{array}$$

5.7 Divide. Remember the steps.

Divide. Multiply. Subtract. Compare. Bring down (or tuck in the number).

a.

$5\overline{)403}$ $6\overline{)90}$ $4\overline{)65}$ $8\overline{)356}$

b.

$3\overline{)270}$ $7\overline{)89}$ $6\overline{)302}$ $9\overline{)639}$

5.8 Look for a pattern to simplify the problem. Solve.

a. 9 + 0 + 4 + 11 = ________   15 + 7 + 5 + 0 = ________

b. 29 x 7 x 0 x 16 = ________   7 x 1 x 10 x 6 = ________

c. 15 + 6 + 4 + 5 = ________   2 + 3 + 17 + 18 = ________

d. 8 x 100 x 7 x 1 = ________   9 x 7 x 1 x 0 = ________

Self Test 5

(each answer, 1 point)

5.01 Use the circle to answer the questions.

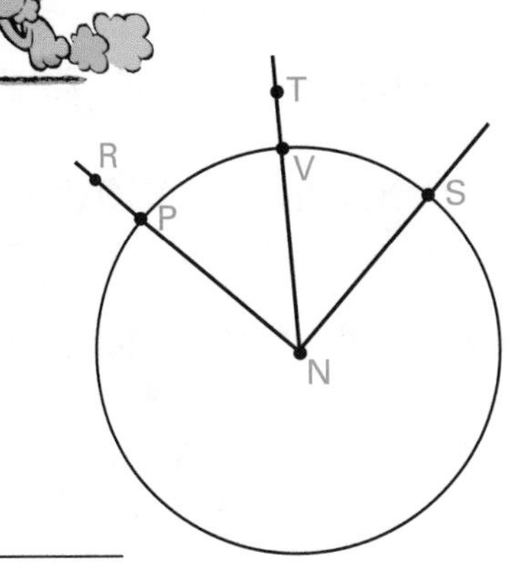

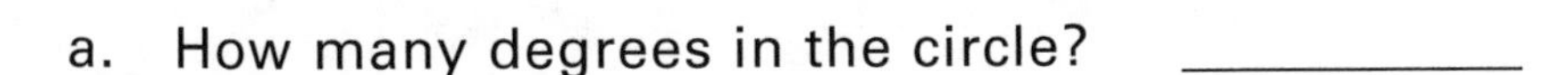

a. How many degrees in the circle? ____________

b. What is point N to angle PNS? ____________

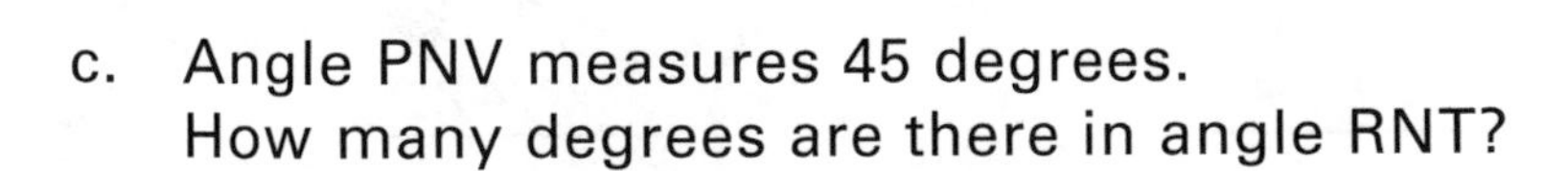

c. Angle PNV measures 45 degrees.
How many degrees are there in angle RNT? ____________

5.02 Find the perimeter and area of the irregular polygon.

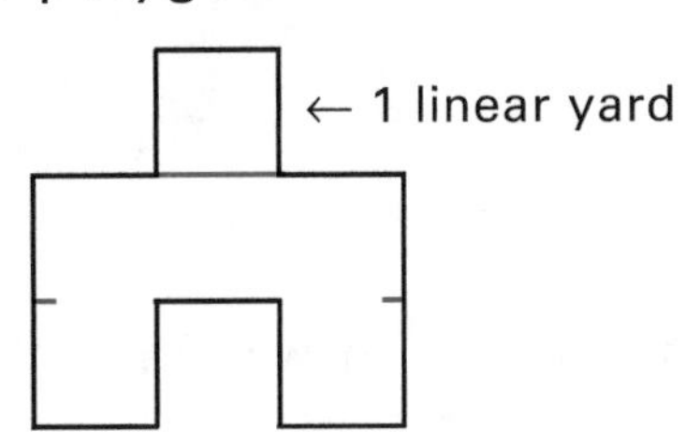

perimeter ____________________

area ____________________

5.03 Julie, Joanne, and Betsy were saving wheatback pennies.
Julie had 27, Joanne had 16, and Lucy had 23.
If they decided to share the coins evenly,
how many pennies would each one receive? ____________

5.04 Add $\frac{1}{3}$ to $\frac{1}{6}$ and multiply by $\frac{5}{12}$. ____________

5.05 Corrine has grown 6 inches this year.
If she is 5 ft. 2 in. tall now, how tall was she last year? ____________

5.06 John was practicing for the track team.
He ran 4 miles on Monday, 6 on Tuesday, 4 on Wednesday,
5 on Thursday, and 6 on Friday. Altogether, he ran 25 miles.

Express the paragraph as an equation.

____

5.07 Judith had 4 dollars, 3 quarters, 1 dime, and 3 pennies
when she went to the store. She had 2 dollars, 4 dimes,
and 1 nickel when she came home.

How much money did Judith spend at the store? ____________
(Express answers in dollars and cents, not in coins.)

5.08 Show three ways to write 42 divided by 7. __________ __________ __________
(each answer, 1 point)

5.09 Write the answer in Arabic numerals. (1 point)

CCLVIII – CXXXIV = ______________ – ______________ = ________________

5.010 Multiply. (each answer, 1 point)

$$\begin{array}{r} 354 \\ \times\ 63 \\ \hline \end{array} \qquad \begin{array}{r} 298 \\ \times\ 507 \\ \hline \end{array} \qquad \begin{array}{r} 6{,}285 \\ \times\ 42 \\ \hline \end{array}$$

5.011 Divide. (each answer, 1 point)

$7\overline{)352}$ $\qquad 6\overline{)578}$ $\qquad 9\overline{)810}$

5.012 Look for the pattern. Solve. (each answer, 1 point)

a. 26 + 0 + 15 + 34 = __________ 5 x 1 x 10 x 3 = __________

b. 9 + 8 + 22 + 11 = __________ 4 x 0 x 8 x 17 = __________

c. 53 + 16 + 0 + 7 = __________ 100 x 4 x 6 x 1 = __________

21/26

My Score ______________

Teacher Check ______________